THE ASSERTIVENESS WORKBOOK
A plan for busy women

JOANNA GUTMANN is a training consultant specializing in interpersonal skills. She is experienced in the subject of assertive communication having designed and run successful training sessions for those who wish to improve their dealings with others both in the office and at home. With this book she brings her proven course to a wider audience.

Joanna runs a variety of interpersonal skills and customer care courses for companies throughout the country.

Overcoming Common Problems Series

For a full list of titles please contact
Sheldon Press, Marylebone Road, London NW1 4DU

The Assertiveness Workbook
A plan for busy women
JOANNA GUTMANN

Beating the Comfort Trap
DR WINDY DRYDEN AND JACK
GORDON

Birth Over Thirty Five
SHEILA KITZINGER

Body Language
How to read others' thoughts by their
gestures
ALLAN PEASE

Body Language in Relationships
DAVID COHEN

Calm Down
How to cope with frustration and anger
DR PAUL HAUCK

Cancer – A Family Affair
NEVILLE SHONE

Comfort for Depression
JANET HORWOOD

Coping Successfully with Hayfever
DR ROBERT YOUNGSON

Coping Successfully with Migraine
SUE DYSON

Coping Successfully with Pain
NEVILLE SHONE

Coping Successfully with PMS
KAREN EVENNETT

Coping Successfully with Panic Attacks
SHIRLEY TRICKETT

**Coping Successfully with Prostate
Problems**
ROSY REYNOLDS

**Coping Successfully with Your
Hyperactive Child**
DR PAUL CARSON

**Coping Successfully with Your Irritable
Bowel**
ROSEMARY NICOL

**Coping Successfully with Your Second
Child**
FIONA MARSHALL

Coping with Anxiety and Depression
SHIRLEY TRICKETT

Coping with Blushing
DR ROBERT EDELMANN

Coping with Bronchitis and Emphysema
DR TOM SMITH

Coping with Candida
SHIRLEY TRICKETT

Coping with Chronic Fatigue
TRUDIE CHALDER

Coping with Cot Death
SARAH MURPHY

Coping with Crushes
ANITA NAIK

Coping with Cystitis
CAROLINE CLAYTON

Coping with Depression and Elation
DR PATRICK McKEON

Coping with Postnatal Depression
FIONA MARSHALL

Coping with Psoriasis
PROFESSOR RONALD MARKS

Coping with Schizophrenia
DR STEVEN JONES AND DR FRANK
TALLIS

Coping with Strokes
DR TOM SMITH

Coping with Suicide
DR DONALD SCOTT

Coping with Thyroid Problems
DR JOAN GOMEZ

Coping with Thrush
CAROLINE CLAYTON

Curing Arthritis Exercise Book
MARGARET HILLS AND JANET
HORWOOD

Curing Arthritis Diet Book
MARGARET HILLS

Curing Arthritis – The Drug-Free Way
MARGARET HILLS

Overcoming Common Problems Series

Curing Arthritis
More ways to a drug-free life
MARGARET HILLS

Curing Illness – The Drug-Free Way
MARGARET HILLS

Depression
DR PAUL HAUCK

Divorce and Separation
Every woman's guide to a new life
ANGELA WILLANS

Don't Blame Me!
How to stop blaming yourself and other
people
TONY GOUGH

**Everything Parents Should Know About
Drugs**
SARAH LAWSON

**Family First Aid and Emergency
Handbook**
DR ANDREW STANWAY

Getting Along with People
DIANNE DOUBTFIRE

Getting the Best for Your Bad Back
DR ANTHONY CAMPBELL

Good Stress Guide, The
MARY HARTLEY

Heart Attacks – Prevent and Survive
DR TOM SMITH

Helping Children Cope with Bullying
SARAH LAWSON

Helping Children Cope with Divorce
ROSEMARY WELLS

Helping Children Cope with Grief
ROSEMARY WELLS

Hold Your Head Up High
DR PAUL HAUCK

How to Be Your Own Best Friend
DR PAUL HAUCK

How to Cope when the Going Gets Tough
DR WINDY DRYDEN AND JACK
GORDON

How to Cope with Bulimia
DR JOAN GOMEZ

How to Cope with Difficult People
ALAN HOUEL WITH CHRISTIAN
GODEFROY

How to Cope with Splitting Up
VERA PEIFFER

How to Cope with Stress
DR PETER TYRER

How to Cope with your Child's Allergies
DR PAUL CARSON

How to Do What You Want to Do
DR PAUL HAUCK

How to Improve Your Confidence
DR KENNETH HAMBLY

How to Interview and Be Interviewed
MICHELE BROWN AND GYLES
BRANDRETH

How to Keep Your Cholesterol in Check
DR ROBERT POVEY

How to Love and Be Loved
DR PAUL HAUCK

How to Pass Your Driving Test
DONALD RIDLAND

How to Stand up for Yourself
DR PAUL HAUCK

**How to Start a Conversation and Make
Friends**
DON GABOR

How to Stop Smoking
GEORGE TARGET

How to Stop Worrying
DR FRANK TALLIS

How to Survive Your Teenagers
SHEILA DAINOW

How to Untangle Your Emotional Knots
DR WINDY DRYDEN AND JACK
GORDON

How to Write a Successful CV
JOANNA GUTMANN

Hysterectomy
SUZIE HAYMAN

Is HRT Right for You?
DR ANNE MACGREGOR

The Incredible Sulk
DR WINDY DRYDEN

The Irritable Bowel Diet Book
ROSEMARY NICOL

The Irritable Bowel Stress Book
ROSEMARY NICOL

Overcoming Common Problems Series

Overcoming Common Problems

THE ASSERTIVENESS WORKBOOK

A plan for busy women

Joanna Gutmann

First published in Great Britain
Sheldon Press, SPCK, Marylebone Road, London NW1 4DU

Second impression 1995

British Library Cataloguing-in-Publication Data
A catalogue record for this book is available from the British Library
ISBN 0–85969–677–4

Photoset by Deltatype Ltd, Ellesmere Port, Cheshire
Printed and bound in Great Britain by
Biddles Ltd, Guildford and King's Lynn

Contents

1

Introduction

Have you ever had trouble getting your family to see your point of view? Have you wasted sleep over having to take back a faulty item to a shop? Is it difficult to get your colleagues at work to hear what you are saying? Do you always get left to do the school run? If any of these sound familiar you will already be aware of the need for assertive skills.

Assertive communication leads to better and easier dealings with those around you. By expressing yourself clearly and directly, you increase your chances of getting your point across. Add to this an increased ability to stand up for yourself and an awareness of the interests of others and you will find misunderstandings and disagreements are reduced.

An assertive approach does not guarantee that you 'win' (although it does increase your chances!). However, when you do not get your own way you will at least end the encounter with your self-esteem intact and without the double blow of guilt or shame over anger, tears or just not speaking out.

By definition, assertiveness encourages a positive frame of mind. It helps you to avoid the tendency to dwell on problems, shortcomings and the thing you 'should have said' and encourages you to look at yourself realistically and work towards taking situations forward positively.

Assertive skills are for anyone and everyone. Do not be fooled into thinking that assertiveness is only for high-powered managers and career women. The skills are invaluable with your partner, family, with friends and, if you work, with colleagues, managers and staff. It takes the same skills to say 'No' to a friend who wants you to collect her children from school as to a manager who wants you to work late.

What are assertive skills?

Assertive skills enable you to say what you feel, need or want in a confident manner but without putting others down in doing so. The less productive alternatives fall into the broad groups of *non-assertive* behaviour (not standing up for yourself or doing so in a way

1

that is easily ignored) or *aggressive* behaviour (standing up for yourself but at the expense of the needs or feelings of others).

Assertive communication is a positive style that involves stating clearly what you would like to happen, but not demanding that it does.

It is important to realize that the word 'assertive' does not describe a person. It describes that person's behaviour at a particular time or in particular circumstances. For example, it is quite possible to be assertive with friends but non-assertive with your partner. Similarly, you may behave aggressively with subordinates whilst not speaking up for yourself with your manager.

Julie found it easy to say which film she wanted to see when out with colleagues from work but always deferred to the wishes of her boyfriend when they went out together. She resented having to sit through films she did not enjoy and used to make negative comments about his taste.

When she thought about it, she realized her behaviour was caused by the fact that she and her boyfriend had not been together long and that she was trying to please him. Indeed, her complaints about the films had the opposite effect and by changing her behaviour and stating her needs before they went to the cinema they were able to find films they both enjoyed or to compromise and alternate between films that each wanted to see.

Sally was happy with her assertiveness with family and friends but when she returned to a part-time job after her youngest child started school, she found it difficult to assert herself. She regularly made mistakes and felt foolish in front of the others in the office.

When Sally studied 'Rights' she realized that she was not accepting her Right not to understand or to make mistakes. She began to ask for clarification when she was given instructions instead of just doing her best with insufficient information. This alone reduced the number of mistakes she made. When she accepted that no one is perfect she was less hard on herself when she did get it wrong and tried to learn instead of wallowing in self-pity and misery. The number of mistakes she made dropped rapidly and she is now a happy member of the team.

If you feel comfortable in a situation, for example with a group of friends or colleagues, you are more likely to behave assertively. It is easy to explain what you want or how you feel in a situation where others respect and welcome you. It is harder to maintain that assertiveness in tougher situations, for example when complaining in a shop or in the face of criticism at work or at home.

Developing your assertive skills will help you to cope with these difficult situations in a clear and calm manner that will increase your chances of making your viewpoint heard and getting it accepted. It also helps improve your dealings with others on an everyday level and simply smooths the path wherever you go.

The process is like improving your fitness. You do not attend one aerobic exercise class and find you are fit. You have to develop from your initial level of fitness in the style and at the pace that suits you. Similarly, you are unlikely to become assertive after one short section. The skills are built gradually and the small instances of assertive behaviour are the building blocks for tackling the bigger problems when they occur. If your building blocks are well laid, your final structure will be sound. This book will guide you through laying those foundations as well as helping you when problems occur.

How to use this book

This book has been devised to enable busy people to learn to become more assertive. Instead of having to take time off work or away from the home to attend a course or evening classes, this simple and straightforward workbook approach enables you to develop and improve your skills within a month by spending just 30–40 minutes each day.

This workbook style combines the best of both worlds: a successful course which deals with issues that are directly relevant to you, but studied at a time and place to suit your needs.

You do not have to reach the end of the workbook before you are able to put the techniques into practice. Very soon you will be able to start making small changes to the way you behave and these simple steps are the sound foundations upon which assertive skills are built.

This enables you to receive assertiveness training to fit in with your lifestyle. It is best to study at a time when you are unlikely to be interrupted and when you feel bright and alert: for night-owls, this will be the evening, perhaps while the children do their homework or when they are in bed. For larks, it may be best to get up 40 minutes earlier, make a cup of tea and settle down to half-an-hour's work before the rest of the family wake. When are you at your best?

The workbook has been designed for study alone, but if a friend is also using it, you might find it useful to work together and compare notes as you go. Do make sure that you choose someone you are comfortable with – there is little benefit in working with someone with whom you cannot assert yourself!

The flexibility of the workbook means that you can work steadily through it or spend longer on the Sections that you find most difficult. Do not be afraid to go back over Sections that seemed simple on paper but prove difficult in reality.

The workbook is split into eighteen Sections, each designed to be 30–40 minutes of study. This timing is only a guide because the relevance of each topic to you and the ease with which you can identify with it are just two of the factors which affect the amount of time needed.

The Sections include information on each aspect of assertiveness, examples and exercises. The early sections give you a sound understanding of the behaviour styles and you will quickly move on to building your skills, improving your dealings with others, starting with the simple aspects and building up to structures for handling more complex problems. Throughout the workbook you are helped to put the skills into practice immediately.

Do not be afraid to write in the book – that's what it's for! It is designed to be your reference book and to guide you through situations that are difficult for you or where you want to change your behaviour. Like a diary it will be intensely personal, and should be as private as you want it to be.

The text

Every Section has a page or two of text to explain the various aspects of assertive behaviour. You should read through this carefully as it forms the basis for the examples, exercises and action points that follow. The text will also prove useful for later reference and perhaps to return to for further thought as your knowledge and skills increase.

Thought bubbles

If you find that thoughts or ideas flash across your mind, only to be forgotten a few minutes later, these are for you! They are random

4

spaces to note down these thoughts (perhaps examples, comments with which you disagree or to highlight a point that is particularly relevant to you) so that you can consider them later when you have finished the bit that you are working on. If there isn't a bubble where you need it, just use the margin!

Examples

Throughout the book, examples from a variety of Sections are given to aid understanding. Read through these, comparing them to your experience, and try to think of similar examples based on your family, friends and work. Add examples of your own as this will make the workbook even more relevant to you.

The exercises

The exercises form the bridge between the theory and the reality of your situation. Don't be afraid to add in an extra example if you are aware that there is a particular area that is relevant to you, and consider how you should respond.

It is essential that you complete the exercises in writing, rather than just read through them and acknowledge that you know what they are getting at. When you actually put pen to paper you will find that you have to be specific in your thoughts and words and this is an essential part of developing your skills.

Suggested answers are given but don't worry about getting answers 'right' or 'wrong' to the last word; no one is going to judge or mark your work. You will know whether you are basically on the right lines or whether you have been, for example, wordy and non-assertive.

If your answers do differ dramatically, go back over them and amend what you have written so that it becomes more assertive, but retains your style.

Putting it into practice

At the end of most Sections, there are hints for applying the content to your everyday life. Together with the last Section 'Taking it forward', they will guide you in developing your assertive skills.

Do not be afraid to add in your own thoughts and plans – remember it is *your* workbook and you are working to improving *your* skills.

Assertiveness – a woman's problem?

Not the case at all. Many men have gained by studying assertive skills in order to improve their communication and management skills. However, assertiveness is still often considered a women's issue – perhaps because women have the perception to recognize that their behaviour affects their success and the courage to take responsibility for making changes!

To use 'he/she' and 'him/her' throughout this book proved too cumbersome. Since I anticipate that most readers will be female, I have resorted to writing it from the woman's point of view. Male readers should have no problem in 'translating' the examples but if it causes any offence please accept my apologies.

What now?

Well, when you get to the end of the Section you will have completed your first day's study. Easy wasn't it!

- Now, identify the time of day when you could best fit in 40 minutes of uninterrupted work.

	First Choice	Second Choice	Third Choice
Early morning?	☐	☐	☐
Coffee time?	☐	☐	☐
Lunch time?	☐	☐	☐
Afternoon?	☐	☐	☐
Evening?	☐	☐	☐
Other?	☐	☐	☐

- Go back over the list and mark the time when you are most alert. Do the two match? If not, how can you reschedule just for the month?
- Now get your diary and plan when you could do the work each day. Be realistic. You are likely to find there are days when you have to work at a different time from your ideal or days when you can't hope to fit in the work at all. It is better to accept this and plan realistically than intend to do the work on a busy day and

then fail to keep up with your schedule, particularly if you are easily demoralized.

- Jot down the dates when you plan to complete each Section below. If you prefer, just plan this week (but remember to plan next week as you get near). Don't worry if the headings make no sense to you; everything will become clear as the month passes.

Introduction	Done today! ....
In preparation	....
Rights	....
Non-assertive behaviour	....
Aggressive behaviour	....
Assertive behaviour	....
Compliments	....
Making requests	....
Refusing requests	....
Handling put-downs	....
Receiving criticism	....
Giving criticism	....
People problems	....
Tackling a problem	....
Reactions to your assertiveness	....
Overcoming the barriers	....
Taking it forward	....

Don't worry if you can't keep up with your plans and have to reschedule. A planned approach is like a diet where one doughnut doesn't mean failure. It is only a slip and the diet can restart immediately. If you do fall behind, replan realistically and aim to stick to the revised version.

All that remains is to say have fun – assertiveness is an enjoyable skill as well as a useful one.

2

In preparation

The following questionnaire is *not* 'How assertive am I now?' Because assertiveness varies according to the time, place and circumstances, such a quiz would have little value. The questions are designed to help you define your behaviour before becoming involved in the various sections of the workbook.

Complete them honestly (you are only cheating yourself if you try to guess a 'right' answer – there isn't one!). If none of the alternatives match your behaviour then add one of your own. Also add any thoughts, similar examples or other relevant notes as you go. You will be using these for reference throughout the book, usually when planning how to apply the individual sections to your life.

1. *When I am paid a compliment I am:*

   ☐ Pleased

   ☐ Surprised

   ☐ Embarrassed

   ☐ Used to it, it happens often

2. *In response to a compliment I say things like 'I've had it for ages . . .' or 'I got it in the sales . . .':*

   ☐ Usually

   ☐ Often

   ☐ Seldom

3. *When I have to ask for help I feel:*

   ☐ Awkward – they may be busy

   ☐ A bit of a failure

   ☐ No problem; they will help me

4. *When I admit to not understanding, I feel:*

   ☐ Stupid

   ☐ That the explanation/instructions are lacking

   ☐ I don't admit it.

5. *The people I find most difficult to ask (or I avoid asking) are:*

   1 .... (name)

   2 .... (name

6. *I find them difficult because:*

   1 ....

   ....

   2 ....

   ....

7. *I feel I have to do as others ask me:*

   ☐ Usually

   ☐ Depends on who they are

   ☐ Only if I want to

8. *If the following people ask me for help, information, etc. I find it difficult to refuse:*

   1 .... (name)

   2 .... (name)

9. *Why is it difficult to refuse?* ....

   ....

10. *The last occasion I, or my work, was criticized was:* ....

    ....

11. *During and after the criticism, I felt:*

    During ....

    After ....

12. *The last occasion I criticized someone was:* ....

    ....

13. *They reacted by:* ....

    ....

14. *The people who, in general, cause me most aggravation are:*

    1 .... (name)

    2 .... (name)

    3 .... (name)

15. *A specific example of the aggravation each causes me is:*

    1 ....

    ....

    2 ....

    ....

    3 ....

    ....

Theory

3

Rights

What are Rights?

The Oxford Dictionary defines a Right as 'What is just, a fair claim or treatment, something one is entitled to.' In terms of assertiveness, the Rights you give yourself and others form the basis of how you behave and communicate.

How Rights relate to assertive behaviour

If you *give Rights* to another that you do not take for yourself, you are behaving non-assertively. For example, excusing the mistakes of others with 'He's only young' or 'She probably didn't think', but reviewing your own mistakes with 'I should have known better' or 'I'll never get it right'.

If you *take Rights* for yourself that you do not give to another, you are behaving aggressively. For example, you might choose not to assert yourself and keep quiet rather than disagree with someone's views. This in itself presents no problem but if you then tell a colleague to 'stand up for yourself, say something . . .' you are not respecting their right to choose not to assert themselves; the Right you took for yourself.

Who gives you your Rights in assertiveness?

In short, you do! Your self-esteem and beliefs about yourself affect the way you behave. If you lack confidence, you are naturally going to find it harder to stand up for yourself.

In order to adopt an assertive approach you need to be clear about the general Rights you give yourself and the way they relate to the Rights you give others.

The following are general Rights in the context of assertive behaviour:

The Right to your own feelings, needs and opinions and to have them respected by others.

You have the Right to express your views when you wish without having to justify yourself to others. Everyone sees things differently

13

and it is important to get away from the idea that if one party is right, everyone else is wrong.

'I liked that film.'

'I think that she is right, and that we should . . .'

The Right to consider your own needs.

This does not mean that you can absolve yourself from all responsibility to others. Rather that you should consider your needs and the extent to which they are met. This will enable you to recognize when you are putting others' needs before yours and decide whether you wish to do something about it.

'I can't meet tonight because I want to . . .'

The Right to ask (not to demand).

A clear request is much fairer to the other person and yet it can feel blunt and perhaps rude to the person who is asking. Instead we resort to hints and veiled comments and then are upset when they are ignored.

'Please can you . . .'

'Are you able to . . .'

The Right to refuse.

Taking your needs into consideration you may wish to refuse the request of another. It is kinder to both parties to do so clearly and politely than to lead the other person on and then eventually find an excuse. If you do not have the Right to refuse, through your Contract of Employment for example, you do retain the Right to explain the difficulties it will cause and/or any problems you can foresee. Although you may be overruled, you can draw comfort from your clear and calm assessment of the situation.

'I'm sorry, I can't.'

'I would rather not share the office. I don't think we can fit in another desk, terminal, and so on.'

The Right not to understand.

If you have ever been part of a conversation and been completely lost, you will know the feeling of not wishing to appear stupid by your inability to grasp the point. Everyone's communication style is different and there is no shame in having to ask for clarification. You will never learn unless you have the courage to admit a lack of knowledge. Remember it is not necessarily you being 'thick', it may well be the other person's inability to explain clearly!

'I'm not clear on the last part, could you clarify it?'

The Right to be successful.

Whether your success is in a high-powered job or on an apparently lower level (e.g. losing a couple of pounds in weight, making a difficult telephone call) you should acknowledge your achievement, to yourself at least, and not play it down if others compliment you.

The Right to make a mistake.

This is easy to agree with in principle but most people cringe when they make a mistake and blow the event out of all proportion. However much we would like to be, no one is perfect and anyone can get it wrong. One piece of incompetent behaviour does not make us an incompetent person and it is important to keep our mistakes in proportion and not dwell on them, compounding a negative self-image.

The Right to change your mind.

Circumstances change, more information becomes available or a snap decision seems wrong with the passing of time. You should not have to defend your decision to change your mind to anyone who thinks it a weakness; in fact it is a strength.

The Right to choose not to assert yourself.

There is no rule that says you must assert yourself at all times. You are free to choose to act non-assertively and not stand up for your Rights. It is important however that you have the confidence to assert yourself when you want to or you will find that the little chips to your self-esteem can wear it away altogether.

The Right to be your own self.

This involves choosing your own destiny; who you marry (or not), where you live, hobbies and interests, etc.

Responsibilities

In order to prevent aggressive behaviour, it is essential to balance these Rights with the Responsibility that goes with them. You have dual Responsibilities in terms of assertiveness.

To respect the personal Rights of others.

It is possible to become so concerned with your own Rights that you lose sight of the Rights of others and act aggressively. The Rights you take for yourself, you should give others (to prevent aggression) and the rights you give to others, you should take for yourself (to prevent non-assertion).

To assert your Rights in a reasonable and responsible manner.

It would be counter-productive to be rigid in defending your Rights at all times and you may choose not to assert yourself on various minor issues. The important thing is that your non-assertion is a conscious decision rather than an inability to assert yourself.

To give an example: you have the Right to make mistakes. This is balanced with the Responsibility to:

- admit your mistake (either to yourself or to others depending on the situation);
- correct it and to be clear about what went wrong so you do not repeat it;
- allow others to make mistakes without humiliating them.

ASSERTIVE BEHAVIOUR INVOLVES BEING CLEAR ABOUT THE RIGHTS YOU TAKE FOR YOURSELF AND RESPECTING THE RIGHTS OF OTHERS

Exercise

For each of the Rights listed below, think of a specific example of either:

(a) when you stood up for this Right;   or
(b) when you did not stand up for this Right.

When you have done this, note any people with whom it is

particularly difficult to stand up for your rights (and those with whom it is easy).

Before you begin, read through the example below.

Example

The Right to consider my own needs
I stood up for this Right when I insisted on sitting down for half an hour before making the tea (I felt very tired).
Or
I did not stand up for this Right when I agreed to drive the children to football practice although I missed the programme on television that I wanted to see.

The Right to your own feelings, etc., and to have them respected by others.

I stood up/did not stand up for this Right when ....

....

The Right to consider your own needs.

I stood up/did not stand up for this Right when ....

....

The Right to ask.

I stood up/did not stand up for this Right when ....

....

The Right to refuse.

I stood up/did not stand up for this Right when ....

....

The Right not to understand.

I stood up/did not stand up for this Right when ....

....

The Right to be successful.

I stood up/did not stand up for this Right when ....

....

The Right to make a mistake.

I stood up/did not stand up for this Right when ....

....

The Right to change your mind.

I stood up/did not stand up for this Right when ....

....

The Right to choose not to assert yourself.

I stood up/did not stand up for this Right when ....

....

The Right to be your own self.

I stood up/did not stand up for this Right when ....

....

When you have completed the exercise, consider the following points. You may like to make notes below.

There were ten Rights. In how many instances did you give an example of standing up for your Rights?

....

In how many instances did you give an example of *not* standing up for your Rights?

....

Do your examples show any general areas or situations where you find it easy to stand up for rights?

e.g. *When it affects my money.*
    When it affects my children.

....

And anywhere you find it particularly difficult?
e.g. *When I am dealing with someone 'more important' than me.*
    When I am at work.

....

Note the names of any people (at home, at work or in any other situation) with whom you find it difficult to stand up for your Rights. You may find it helps to give reasons or examples.

....

....

....

....

....

....

Now note the names of those with whom it is easy to stand up for your Rights; again with reasons or examples.

....

....

....

....

....

....

There are no right or wrong answers to the questions above. Your thoughts on them will help you identify your behaviour styles in different situations as you work through the book.

Putting it into practice

- Watch yourself over the next few days and note examples of Rights in practice. Which Rights are you and others standing up for? Which are you not? What are the effects?

Make notes below:

4

Non-assertive behaviour

How often have you found yourself watching a film you did not want to see or helping a friend when you did not want to? Just because you did not like to say no.

Non-assertive behaviour involves:

- Saying what you want but in an apologetic manner so that it loses its impact.

  'I know I'm new to this but . . .'
  'Excuse me for mentioning this but . . .'

- Putting yourself down.

  'I'm only a housewife.'
  'You know what I'm like – I can never get this right.'

- Not stating your views.

  Saying yes when you would rather say no.
  Responding with 'I don't mind' when you do have a preference.

The trouble is that when people agree with our apparent low opinion of ourselves, either directly or indirectly, we are hurt and our self-confidence is damaged still further.

Generally, in behaving non-assertively or passively, we are trying to please others, to save trouble or to avoid conflict. However, the effect is often the opposite; people will find it easier to deal with us if they know what we want and become annoyed at indecision and lack of clarity.

Non-verbal indicators include lack of eye contact, defensive posture, fidgeting and a general appearance of lack of confidence with a giggly, hesitant or whining tone.

Verbal indicators include the examples shown above together with 'fillers' (um, er); negative approach ('I don't suppose . . .') and most commonly confusing the statement with additional comments. For example, 'I'm sorry to trouble you, but COULD I HAVE A LIFT INTO TOWN WITH YOU TOMORROW? I hope you don't mind me asking, I normally wouldn't trouble you but my car has to go in for service and you know what the buses are like round here.'

How you come to be non-assertive

As we see below, the immediate effect of non-assertive behaviour may well be pleasant and thus encourage you to continue behaving in this way. Some of the other reasons include confusing non-assertive behaviour with politeness, kindness and helpfulness, a fear of unpleasantness, not thinking rationally about yourself or seeing the only alternative behaviour as aggression.

Effects of non-assertion

On the situation

You will become committed to courses of action that do not meet the needs of both parties, e.g. weak compromises, impractical solutions, or just plain 'getting lumbered' with one or both parties feeling unhappy about the result.

Short-term effect on you

Following non-assertive behaviour you may feel relieved that you have avoided a scene or upsetting someone, although you may feel sorry for yourself for having got into a situation that you had not intended. You may quite enjoy being a martyr and gaining 'brownie points'. These immediate effects are not necessarily unpleasant and are fairly safe and thus can encourage you to behave non-assertively in the future. However there is a danger that if you bottle up your anger and resentment, you are likely to fly off the handle at some small problem and start a row over nothing. All the old niggles and crimes are dragged up and before you know where you are you have a full-scale row. For example.

> *'What wine did you buy?'*
> *'Oh hell, I forgot. I'll nip round to the off-licence now.'*
> *'You always forget, can't I trust you with the simplest thing? I work all day too and yet I have to plan what we eat, when we eat it, where and when to buy it, how to cook it and if I'm lucky you might deign to wash up occasionally. You may offer to help but you never do anything.'*

Long-term effects on you

Persistent non-assertive behaviour results in a loss of self-esteem and confidence in dealing with problems, which may lead to your becoming angry with yourself and a feeling of general frustration and failure – all creating an internal tension which, if in turn is not released, can in the extreme cause illness.

Effect of your non-assertive behaviour on others

Initially, people may feel sorry for you but eventually they lose respect for you and may find your lack of assertion irritating. The thoughts you have of trying to be 'nice' and to please have just the opposite effect.

Exercise

Identify three examples of recent non-assertive behaviour. The examples should be specific; e.g. 'I agreed to make three cakes for Jane's produce stall last weekend', not 'Jane always manages to talk me into helping her'.

For each one, detail the positive and negative effect of your non-assertion on you.

I felt 'noble' at putting myself out. (Positive)

I spent all Friday evening baking. (Negative)

Example: ....

Positive effect: ....

Negative effect: ....

Example: ....

Positive effect: ....

Negative effect: ....

Example: ....

Positive effect: ....

Negative effect: ....

Putting it into practice

• Note examples of your own and others' non-assertive behaviour. What effect did it have on your feelings? What effect did it have on the outcome of the situation?

Make notes below:

5

Aggressive behaviour

The *Oxford English Dictionary* defines aggressive as 'apt to make attacks, showing aggression' and the word is commonly associated with anger, shouting, argument and so on. In the context of assertive behaviour, however, it means taking Rights for yourself that you do not allow to others.

It also includes the behaviour of the friend who knows you are rushing to get away, but insists on showing you her photographs. Although friendly, she is ignoring your Rights. Aggressive behaviour also includes 'friendly' advice such as 'You should try . . .', 'You must tell him . . .' or 'Why didn't you. . . ?'

Aggressive behaviour may first appear to be non-assertion; for example, a friend who asks for your help with 'Could you do me a huge favour? As you are so good at typing figures/sewing/drawing, could you do this? It will only take a few minutes but I never was any good at it.' It is much harder to say no in the face of the flattery, the short time needed and so on, and thus the other person is abusing your Right to be asked clearly and to say no. This is manipulative aggression.

Aggressive behaviour is not necessarily intentional. A self-confident person who is used to getting their own way may not think about the needs/feelings of others. Conversely, lack of confidence can make us abrupt and appear aggressive.

Non-verbal indicators include glaring eyes; leaning forward in an overbearing way; pointing finger and raised voice. Manipulative aggression will often appear to be non-assertive behaviour (pleading tone, etc.).

Verbal indicators include threats; put downs; sarcasm and prejudice (e.g. 'Typical woman'). Manipulative aggression will usually take the form of grovelling or self put-down, but with the intention of ensuring that you give in.

How you come to be aggressive

In some organizations managers are promoted because their aggression is seen as firm leadership by other aggressive managers, especially when they may move on in a couple of years time before the long-term effects of their management style become evident.

Other reasons for aggressive behaviour include a belief that aggression is the alternative to non-assertive behaviour, seeing people or situations as a threat, over-reacting to a previous experience or a belief that aggressive behaviour gains respect from others.

The effect of aggressive behaviour

On the outcome of the situation

The needs of both parties are not met so people may well feel resentful about the outcome and solutions that are 'agreed' may turn out not to happen.

Short-term effect on you

You may feel a release of tension immediately after behaving aggressively. You may feel proud that you have got your own way and feel a sense of power over others; both feelings that may reinforce your aggressive behaviour. Others may encourage you by remarks like 'You certainly put him in his place'; so again the dilemma, the initial feelings are rewarding but the long-term effects can cause permanent damage to effectiveness.

Long-term effect on you

If used as the main alternative to non-assertive behaviour, you may feel guilty for which you compensate by being duly apologetic or over-helpful for a while. On the other hand you may start to put the blame for your 'difficult time' on others, perceiving them as being on the attack. This is time-consuming and drains your nervous energy, causing problems in maintaining friendships.

Effect of aggression on others

Some people may openly return your aggression by making similar remarks, threats, sarcasm, non-cooperation, etc. Some will go underground, saying one thing to your face but doing another, making it difficult for your ideas to be carried out in practice.

It can be seen that the reasons for non-assertive and aggressive behaviour are very similar we may swing from one to another, snapping and behaving aggressively then feeling guilty and being non-assertive and compliant to make up for it before snapping again.

Exercise

Identify two occasions when you have behaved aggressively *or* when others have done so to you. Remember that aggressive behaviour is not necessarily loud or angry – it is simply the ignoring of personal rights. As with the previous exercise, the examples should be specific.

For each, note the Right that was abused and the effect that the behaviour had on you, positive (e.g. 'I gave as good as I got' or 'I earned brownie points') and/or negative (e.g. 'I felt guilty' or 'I was humiliated').

Example: ....

Right(s) abused: ....

Effect on me: ....

Example: ....

Right(s) abused: ....

Effect on me: ....

Putting it into practice

- Note examples of your own and others' aggressive behaviour.

What effect did it have on your feelings? What effect did it have on the outcome of the situation?

Make notes below:

6

Assertive behaviour

Assertive behaviour aims to deal with a situation in a way which is satisfactory to both parties. It will help you to identify what you want, ask for it clearly, negotiate effectively with other people and develop a self-confident communication style.

Assertive behaviour involves:

- Standing up for what you want and clearly stating your needs.

  'I would like to go out for a drink this evening.'

- Owning your needs or opinions.

  'I would like to see that new thriller, how about you?'
  not
  'Which film do you want to see; that new thriller is supposed to be good?'

- Respecting the Rights of others.

  'I would like to take a holiday during the first week of August; how will that fit in with you?'

How you come to be assertive

A few lucky people are naturally assertive, but most achieve it through hard work and practice. Assertiveness is a skill and thus can be learnt and developed. It is never too late to learn.

Non-verbal indicators include a relaxed but firm stance, steady voice, good eye contact.

The verbal indicators include opinion-seeking ('What is your experience?' 'How do you feel about that?'), personal statements and a lack of 'waffle' without seeming too blunt.

Why be more assertive?

One good reason is that you will become less non-assertive and/or aggressive. You will be more effective in your dealings with others and people will work *with* you rather than *against* you. The outcome of your dealings with others will be more rewarding for both parties and you will develop a more positive approach to life generally.

The more specific reasons are:

A GREATER CHANCE OF GETTING WHAT YOU WANT.

When needs, wants, ideas and opinions are clearly stated, as they are in assertive behaviour, they are more likely to be understood and met. If others are encouraged to express their needs, etc., it is easier to see where there is conflict and take steps to seek common ground where the views can be reconciled.

INCREASE IN SELF-CONFIDENCE.

Achieving a satisfactory solution to a problem by being assertive will increase your self-esteem, giving you confidence to deal with subsequent problems. If your needs are not met, at least you can feel that you have made your point in a reasonable manner and that you have done yourself justice.

GREATER SELF-CONTROL.

Assertive behaviour implies thinking in an objective manner before acting, considering likely consequences and how to deal with possible reactions. You become less likely to behave in a way which you may subsequently regret.

HAVING MORE INFLUENCE.

Ideas expressed in a logical manner with the appropriate behaviour have more chance of being accepted. Even if they are not, you are better able to accept failure and not let it deter you from future assertive behaviour.

REDUCTION IN PERSONAL STRESS.

You will worry less about approaching difficult situations. Your energy will be used positively towards solving the problem and not negatively worrying about the consequence of failure.

Body language

Body language is the gestures, expression, voice tone and other signals which we send all the time and which support our words if we are being honest with ourselves and others.

Although we may not consciously notice body language, it often sends out a more powerful message than the spoken word.

Consider the following examples:

- The friend or partner who says 'No, really, everything is fine' in a strained voice with their teeth clenched and knuckles white.
- The emptiness of the words 'Of course I love you' in a distant voice, avoiding your eyes.

It is practically impossible to assert yourself if you do not make eye contact, if you fidget and if you mumble or hesitate. The next time you talk to someone, hopefully within the next few hours, watch yourself:

- Where are you looking?
- How would you describe your body position?
- Is your voice clear and confident?

If you are to appear assertive and confident, you should look people in the eye – not all the time, staring them out, but maintaining reasonable eye contact rather than gazing out of the window, around the room or at your shoes.

You should make sure that your body is facing them and is open, rather than defensive. This means not curling up in a chair or folding your arms and peering over the top of them.

Your voice should be clear. Good eye contact and body position will help this. Practise by talking into a mirror, saying everyday things to your reflection and working on the appearance of confidence. You will soon be able to project this confident appearance, even if you do not necessarily feel confident.

Exercise

Look at each of the situations below and study the alternative responses. Indicate whether each response is assertive, non-assertive or aggressive. (You will find some answers at the end of the Section.)

A colleague/friend compliments you on a talk you have given. You say:
1. 'Thank you.'

BEHAVIOUR:

2. 'It didn't go to plan, I found it really difficult.'

BEHAVIOUR:

You have booked a day's leave tomorrow to meet a friend who is over from New York. Your colleague decides to take the day off to go shopping for her wedding dress and checks that you will be in. You say:
3. 'Yes, I'll be in, I suppose I can see Susie at the weekend.'

BEHAVIOUR:

4. 'Yes, I'll be in.'

BEHAVIOUR:

You have watched your manager give a good presentation and afterwards congratulate him on his success, saying:
5. 'That was really brilliant; I'd never have the nerve to face so many people.'

BEHAVIOUR:

6. 'That went really well; I like the way you made the statistics interesting.'

BEHAVIOUR:

One of your staff has done some copy-typing. When reading it through, you find six mistakes. You return it to the typist and say:
7. 'I'm sorry to trouble you again, but there are a couple of errors here; could you possibly find time to retype it? I would like to catch the post if possible.'

BEHAVIOUR:

8. 'There are a few errors here; please could you correct them in time for today's post?'

BEHAVIOUR:

A colleague/friend is going to have to face someone who has been unpleasant to her in the past. You say:
9. 'You must stand up to him this time, don't let him get away with being so rude to you and don't let yourself be browbeaten.'

BEHAVIOUR:

10. 'If you want to discuss how you are going to behave when you see her, I'll be happy to help.'

BEHAVIOUR:

You are trying to match a pair of shoes to your new dress and despite the best efforts of the assistant, none of the pairs she offers you are right. You:
11. Thank her, explaining none are right.

BEHAVIOUR:

12. Complain of how useless the shop is.

BEHAVIOUR:

You have made a mistake which will cost your Company around £8,000 to put right. Your boss is reprimanding you and you:
13. Get angry, saying it would not have happened if you had been properly briefed.

BEHAVIOUR:

14. Shift from one foot to another, feeling about three years old.

BEHAVIOUR:

You ring a friend to apologize for being late meeting her for supper last night and say:
15. 'I've rung to apologize for being late last night. I'm sorry for the trouble it caused.'

BEHAVIOUR:

16. 'I've rung to apologize for being late last night. It is always difficult to get to you for 7.30.'

BEHAVIOUR:

Putting it into practice

- Note examples of your own and others' assertive behaviour. What effect did it have on your feelings? What effect did it have on the outcome of the situation?

Make notes below:

Assertive behaviour

1. Assertive.
2. Non-assertive (putting yourself down).
3. Non-assertive (although could be manipulative, thus aggressive, if this reply is intended to make the other person feel guilty or awkward).
4. Non-assertive (not stating your needs).
5. Non-assertive (putting yourself down as much as complimenting the other party).
6. Assertive.
7. Non-assertive (wordy and unclear; the deadline of catching the post could easily be missed).
8. Assertive (no exaggeration; deadline clearly stated).
9. Aggressive (giving no specific help and putting down through emphasis on past failure).
10. Assertive.
11. Assertive.
12. Aggressive.
13. Aggressive (shifting blame on to someone else).
14. Non-assertive.
15. Assertive.
16. Aggressive (shifting blame).

Making a start

7

Compliments

How often have you overheard, or been part of, a conversation like the following:

'That's a lovely skirt.'
'Oh, I've had it for ages.'
'I think it's great, the colour really suits you.'
'It's getting a bit worn now; still, it does for around the house.'

The person who originally paid the compliment has to justify it and ends up snubbed.

The reasons given for shrugging off compliments are usually embarrassment or awkwardness. However, this cumbersome passing of the compliment from one party to the other and back simply adds to the awkwardness.

Almost everyone likes to be complimented and to give a compliment is also a pleasure, particularly when it pleases the receiver. An assertive approach to both giving and receiving compliments will help you to avoid conversations like the one above.

Giving compliments

Make sure that your praise is genuine and keep your compliment clear and simple, using 'I' statements.

'I like that jacket.'

'I think that was a great presentation.'

Make sure you do not fish for a compliment for yourself under the disguise of praising others.

'That was a delicious lunch; I can't do more than boil an egg.'

This usually makes the receiver feel they have to assure you of your culinary skills, rather than accept the compliment that you paid them.

Putting yourself down when complimenting reduces the value of the compliment. Most of us would place greater value on a compliment from a confident person than from someone with such low self-esteem that they would be impressed by any achievement.

Receiving compliments

It is often embarrassment that makes us put ourselves down but it is not 'blowing your own trumpet' to be pleased to receive a compliment. Obviously you do not want to be seen as vain or boastful, but remember your Rights to be successful and accept the compliment graciously.

Avoid bouncing the compliment straight back:
'You're looking great as well';

or deflecting it:
'Thank you but it's Lizzie who is the real expert'.

A short and clear 'Thank you' leaves both parties feeling good. If you do feel the need to add some comment, ensure that it is a positive one.

'What a pretty blouse.'
'Thank you; it's one of my favourites.'

or

'Thank you; I've had it for ages [catch yourself] and always loved it.'

'If your report doesn't win them over, nothing will.'
'Thank you – it took ages but I'm pleased with the result.'

Support what you are saying by the way in which you say it – your body language. Make sure that whether you are giving or receiving compliments you look at the other person and smile at them. Try to avoid diffident shrugs or turning your body away in embarrassment.

Exercise

In addition to the obvious 'Thank you . . .', add a positive response to each of the following compliments.

1. *'What a lovely sweater, did you knit it yourself?'*

   'Thank you; ....

   ....

2. *'You're looking well.'*

   'Thank you; ....

   ....

3. *'That was a lovely lunch.'*

   'Thank you; ....

   ....

4. *'I never mind you driving – I always feel safe.'*

   'Thank you; ....

   ....

5. *'That report was perfect; thanks for doing it so quickly.'*

   'Thank you; ....

   ....

Putting it into practice

- Look at your response to Questions 1 and 2 of Section 2 'In Preparation . . .' and consider your answers in the light of this Section. How do you normally behave when complimented?

   ....

   ....

- What changes should you make to your usual style of response? Be specific and realistic.

....

....

....

- Make sure you compliment someone today or tomorrow, and do so assertively! If you are complimented, respond with pleasure.

Compliments: Model answers

The following are *examples* of answers. It is highly unlikely that you will have these 'word for word' but your answer should be similar in length, not have extra justifying phrases and be similar in tone.

1. 'Thank you; yes I did.'
2. 'Thank you; I've been exercising a bit more.'
3. 'Thank you; I'm glad you enjoyed it.'
4. 'Thank you; I've always enjoyed driving.'
5. 'Thank you; it was fun to do.'

8
Making requests

Do you find it difficult to ask people for help or information? If you do, it is likely that your difficulty means that you do not ask clearly; awkwardness may make you sound abrupt and bossy or confuse your request with explanations and justification.

Some people are easier to ask than others; usually those who say 'Yes' as though they mean it or say 'No' but without awkwardness or arrogance. It is much harder to ask people who agree with an air of unwillingness, those who have let you down before, or those who make you feel stupid for having to ask.

Rights and Responsibilities

You have the Right to:
- ask;
- expect an honest answer;
- change your mind.

You have the Responsibility to:
- ask clearly so that the other person knows what they are taking on;
- be honest about what is required;
- take 'No' for an answer.

General hints

BE DIRECT

Be clear and honest otherwise people will be irritated by your beating around the bush or resentful if they are expected to respond without knowing what is involved.

'Would you be able to help with the school run on Tuesday? I can't be at the school, but I will be back by the time you get home.'

'Debbie, I need the figures for the July returns by next Wednesday; is that possible?'

'Please could you ask Max to ring me when he gets in?'

41

DON'T JUSTIFY

If you get involved in detailed reasons for your requests, you will confuse the issue and appear to be justifying yourself. Of course, it does no harm to give a reason if you wish, but ensure that it is short and honest. Look at the comparative examples below.

> *'My car is in for repair this week. Would you be able to get some washing powder for me?'*

not

> *'I hope you won't think this is a cheek, but I won't have my car this week. If you're going to the supermarket, could you possibly pick up some washing powder for me. I wouldn't normally ask but I must get David's football kit washed.'*

> *'Could you help me by finding out who's coming to the office party? I have to get through all of this today and I must leave at five to get to the dentist.'*

not

> *'I've got to go round and find out who's coming to the office party. With this toothache, all I want to do is hide behind my desk. Now Mark wants this typed by the end of today and there are a heap of phone calls to make. If you're not too busy, could you sort out the party? I want to get away on time or I'll miss my appointment at the dentist and I'm supposed to be going out tonight.'*

DON'T FLATTER PEOPLE INTO A CORNER

'I know you'll help me out' or 'Knowing your skill at dressmaking . . .' are examples of manipulative aggression. By 'selling' your requests in this way you make it difficult for someone to refuse. This might suit you because your request will be met, but the resulting resentment and bad feeling are seldom worth it. Also if you push someone into agreeing to help you when they are not able to, they may well let you down later which is likely to cause greater problems than if they said no to begin with.

DON'T GROVEL

By apologizing for yourself (e.g. 'I'm so sorry to trouble you'), you will only irritate the receiver.

> *'I know I don't know much about it, but . . .'*

> *'I'm only a secretary, but . . .'*

'I know you're very busy, I don't suppose this is important, but . . .'

LET THE OTHER PERSON SAY NO

Ask the question clearly and simply, letting the other person know what is involved. If they refuse you, accept their refusal and don't try to make them change their mind by pressure, flattery or any other means.

Remember that people usually don't like to say no and this may make them appear abrupt or even rude. When you make a request, plan how you will react to a refusal so that you can carry on the conversation without an awkward pause.

'Can you babysit for us on Tuesday; we'll be back by 10.00?'
'I'm sorry, it's my exam on Wednesday and I must revise and get an early night.'
'No problem, and good luck for Wednesday.'

Provided that you have asked clearly and have honestly said what is involved (if applicable), you do not have to take responsibility for the other person if they say yes. However, you may like to pick up on an indication of unwillingness and try to find out if there is a problem.

'Can you babysit for us on Tuesday; we'll be back by 10.00?'
'Oh, let me think, I suppose so.'
'You don't seem sure, is there a problem?'
'Not really, it's just that my exam is first thing on Wednesday morning, but I suppose I can revise at your house.'
'No, leave it, the children don't go to bed until 8.00 and you need an early night – I'll ask Sue – it's no problem.'
'Are you sure? I would be grateful.'

It is far easier to get it out in the open than to face later resentment that her last evening of revision was interrupted or to feel guilty (albeit unnecessarily) if she should fail the exam.

'Could you give me a lift home tonight?'
'Um, yes, I can.'
'You don't seem sure; have you other plans?'
'No, I was only going to call in and see my Mother, I can go tomorrow.'
'Don't worry; could you drop me off at the bus station and I can get the bus out of town?'
'Yes, of course, no problem.'

A workable compromise is reached which again removes the possibility of resentment or bad feeling.

Although you have to plan in advance to begin with, you will soon find that you are able to make requests assertively without any prior thought.

Exercise

Identify the style of the six requests below and then rewrite them assertively.

1. 'I wish you'd get off your backside and lay the table.'

Style: ....

Rewrite in an assertive style: ....

....

2. 'If you're not too busy, would you like to come in for a cup of tea . . . or perhaps next week if you've not got time.'

Style: ....

Rewrite in an assertive style: ....

....

3. 'Since you're such a wonderfully kind boss, you won't mind if I take Friday off will you?'

Style: ....

Rewrite in an assertive style: ....

....

4. 'Do you have time to type this for me? I'd like to get it in the post today; I'm sorry to have to rush you . . . you know what it's like. Thank you ever so much.'

Style: ....

Rewrite in an assertive style: ....

....

5. 'You'll do the bottle stall at the PTA fete, won't you?'

Style: ....

Rewrite in an assertive style: ....

....

6. 'You're the only person I can ask to do this; I can't think of anyone else who will do a decent job of it and I'm hopeless at sewing. This skirt needs shortening . . .'

Style: ....

Rewrite in an assertive style: ....

....

Putting it into practice

- Look back to Questions 3–6 of Section 2 'In Preparation . . .' and consider your answer in the light of this Section. What is your usual style of making requests?

....

....

- What changes should you make to the way you phrase requests? Be specific and realistic.

....

....

....

- Think before you speak and when you next have to make a request, plan what you are going to say.

- Listen to the requests others make of you and identify whether they are assertive, non-assertive, aggressive (or manipulative). What effect does the style have on you?

Making requests: Model answers

The following are *examples* of answers. It is highly unlikely that you will have these 'word for word' but your answer should be similar in length, not have extra justifying phrases, and be similar in tone.

1. Aggressive. 'Please would you lay the table?'
2. Non-assertive. 'Would you like to come in for a drink?'
3. Aggressive. 'Please may I take Friday off?'
4. Non-assertive. 'Could you type this in time for today's post?'
5. Aggressive. 'Please could you run the bottle stall for the PTA fete?'
6. Aggressive (manipulative). 'This skirt needs shortening, could you do it for me?'

9

Refusing requests

How often have you ended up resenting the time you're spending on something you didn't want to do in the first place?

Very few people find it easy to say no without some feelings of guilt and, if we do manage to find the words to refuse someone, we often waste our time and theirs with excuses and justifications. In doing so we leave ourselves open to be pushed into saying yes but then resent it and blame the other party.

Rights and Responsibilities

You have the Right:
- to consider your own needs;
- to say yes or no for yourself.

You have the Responsibility:
- to respect the feelings of the other person.

General hints

SAY NO (NOT MAYBE)

Many people find it hard to say words like 'no', 'can't', 'won't'. As a result they say things like 'that will be rather difficult'. They mean 'no', but the other person may well hear it as a 'definite maybe'; 'that will be rather difficult, but . . .', which is well on the way to saying 'yes'.

Make sure that your refusal is clear. This does not mean that it has to be rude or abrupt. Look at the other person directly and, if appropriate, smile.

'I can't go with you on Friday.'

'No, I don't have the time.'

LISTEN

Listen to the request that the other person is making rather than their tone and behaviour. This will help you clarify what it is they want and enable you to avoid reacting to any aggressive or non-assertive behaviour.

'You can do my school run on Thursday can't you?'
should be treated as 'Please could you do the school run on Thursday?'
and refused by, for example:
'I'm afraid I can't; I have a dental appointment.'

DON'T RAMBLE ON

Obviously you don't wish to seem abrupt, but it's easier for all if you avoid phrases like 'normally I would love to' or 'I do hope you don't mind but . . .'. Over-apologizing comes into this category as well.

The more wordy you are, the greater the chances of misunderstanding; the message you believe you have sent is lost in everything around it and the other person may pick up the message they want to hear – a 'yes', or at least a 'maybe'.

DON'T MAKE EXCUSES

Give a reason if you wish but beware of finding a string of excuses; they will only sound false and may be easily countered.

ASK FOR CLARIFICATION/FURTHER INFORMATION

If you do not know exactly what is expected of you, ask for the further details you need. To say 'I don't know, how much of my time will be needed?' will give you time to decide what you want to do and means that you can base your response on fact; 'I'm sorry, I simply can't spare an afternoon this weekend.'

NEGOTIATE

Be clear about what you do not wish to do, but offer an alternative if it is appropriate.

'Can I borrow that book you've been reading – I can't find it in any of the bookshops?'

'I'm afraid I don't lend books, but let me write down the details and ISBN number then you can order it.'

DON'T BLAME OTHERS

Take responsibility for making your own choices and decisions.

Avoid refusals like:
'I'm sorry, I can't come – you know how David hates me being away at weekends.'

It is your choice as to whether you go out and cope with David's annoyance or whether you stay in and keep the peace. David's behaviour is a factor in your decision, but it is your choice.

ACKNOWLEDGE INVITATIONS

It is difficult to refuse when faced with an invitation that you do not want to accept. Most of us have been guilty of saying things like 'I'll check the diary' or 'I'll see what the others are up to', in order to gain time to think of an excuse. Most people take anything other than no to mean yes, and thus the other person is going ahead on the basis that you will be there and is doubly disappointed when you ring with your reason (excuse?). Something we have done out of a desire to avoid hurting someone causes more trouble than an initial refusal.

To thank the person for inviting you before refusing makes the refusal seem less blunt. For example:
'Thank you for asking us, but I'm afraid we're busy then.'

'Thank you, but I must rush home tonight.'

'Thank you, but I like to get home at lunchtime.'

Saying sorry

There is nothing wrong with using 'I'm sorry . . .' when saying no, provided that it is a simple expression of regret as in 'I'm sorry, I do not have time until tomorrow'. However, be careful that you do not over-apologize and thus weaken your refusal or leave yourself open to be pushed.

Coping with persistence

You may be faced with someone who persists, trying to make you change your mind. They are failing to recognize your Right to refuse. This may take one of the following forms.

PLEADING

'Oh, please – I can't think of anyone else who could do it.'
Respond by simply restating the refusal; e.g. 'I'm sorry that I can't help you'.

PATRONIZING/BULLYING

'Oh, go on – it won't take you long.'
Firmly restate the refusal, avoiding getting into a discussion about the length of time needed; e.g. 'I don't have the time to spare'.

BLAMING

'You're going to get me into trouble.'
Ignore this type of pressure and, again, restate; e.g. 'I certainly don't intend that, but I really can't help you.'

As you can see, the main technique for countering persistence is to repeat your initial refusal, warmly, keeping your speech slow and avoiding any side-tracking argument. This is sometimes known as the 'broken record' technique. For example:

> *'I've arranged to meet my sister for lunch, please could you listen for my phone?'*
> *'I'm sorry, I can't. I'm going out at lunch-time as well.'*
> *'But I must meet her, you know what a bitch she is if she's let down.'*
> *'I have to go out at lunch-time as well.'*
> *'Oh go on, you can do your shopping any time, surely you'll help me out.'*

'I'll always help if I can, but I have to go out at lunch-time as well.'
'Oh well, I'd better ring her; she is not going to like this.'

Exercise

Think of two examples when you've taken on something you didn't want to. Bearing in mind the person who asked you, note down what you could have said to refuse them at the time of the initial request.

Example: ....

Response: ....

....

Example: ....

Response: ....

Putting it into practice

Anticipate a request which may be made to you and plan how you will refuse. The importance of the request doesn't matter.

Request: ....

Response: ....

....

- Refer to Questions 7–9 of Section 2 'In preparation . . .' and consider your answers in the light of this Section. How do you usually react when saying no?

  Body language (eye contact, fidgeting, body position): ....

  ....

  Words I typically use: ....

  ....

- What changes should you make to your style? ....

  ....

  ....

- Next time you want to refuse a request, do so clearly, concisely and firmly.
- Watch the words and behaviour of others as they refuse (or try to!).

10

Handling 'put-downs'

Put-downs are the little digs that sour our relationship with colleagues or friends and can wear us down. They may leave us feeling stung or humiliated or may be very minor; the type of thing that we may feel is not worth making an issue of.

If we let these ride over our needs/feelings (non-assertion) they can lead to a general feeling of discomfort in the company of someone, combined with suppressed annoyance at their behaviour and perhaps at ourselves for not saying anything.

Alternatively, we might make a sharp and perhaps sarcastic response (aggression), sometimes saying something we later regret or alternatively having no effect which merely leaves us feeling impotent.

Neither of these responses is satisfactory in the long term. Either way, we often waste time and energy dwelling on the brilliant reply that we couldn't think of at the time and replaying the scene with ourselves as the hero, cutting the aggressor down to size with a dazzling retort.

It would be wrong to assume that every time anyone makes comments of this type they are 'out to get you'. Generally it is lack of thought or a rather aggressive sense of humour, and if you are not concerned by the comments then there is no point in trying to stop them.

It is important, though, that you are able to respond in a suitable manner when you are annoyed by them.

MAKING DECISIONS FOR YOU

'If I were you . . .'
This can lead to problems if you feel you have to take their advice, either out of politeness or because of their seniority (real or supposed). In responding, you should acknowledge the 'help' being offered; after all, it may be well meant. However you need to assert your Right to consider your own needs and decide for yourself.

> *'Thanks for your advice, but I must sort this out for myself.'*
>
> *'Thank you; I'll bear that in mind.'*

NAGGING

'Haven't you finished that report yet?'
This type of nagging usually slows down the work it is trying to speed up and causes resentment. Ask simply why they want to know – has the deadline changed? This avoids being facetious but unless there is a genuine reason, the pointlessness of the nagging will show.

> *'Why do you ask?'*

PUTTING YOU ON THE SPOT

'Are you busy this afternoon?'
It is unusual for people consciously to put you on the spot by asking this, but if you are to avoid being lumbered, you need to know what they are planning. By asking what is involved before you respond, you will be able to answer honestly.

> *'How much time do you need?'*
> *'What do you have in mind?'*

DESCRIBING YOUR ACTIONS IN EMOTIVE TERMS

'That was an idiotic thing to do.'
If you've made a mistake, you have the Responsibility to admit it. However, you should not be humiliated and you have the Right to put the problem in perspective.

> *'I didn't get it right but I don't believe it was idiotic.'*

54

STEREOTYPING

'All secretaries say that.'
You should emphasize that you wouldn't know about the rest of the stereotype group and emphasize your individuality.

'It's my view; I wouldn't know about other secretaries.'

IMPLYING YOU ARE LYING

'You know that is not true.'
Re-state the facts as you see them, taking responsibility for your own view.

'I believe it is the case.'

LECTURING

'We should co-operate.'
Get details of what the other party has in mind. One-sided co-operation will soon show.

'How do you mean?'

Add your own examples of put-downs here:

....

....

....

Exercise

Prepare a suitable assertive response for each of the following put-downs. Make sure that you are raising yourself up, rather than trying to put the other party down in return.

1. *'In your position, I would . . .'*

....

....

2. *'Isn't lunch ready yet?'*

....

....

3. *'Have you got any free time today?'*

....

....

4. *'Don't be so stupid.'*

....

....

5. *'Typical woman . . .'*

....

....

6. *'Oh come on, you know he didn't say that.'*

....

....

7. *'We must work together on this.'*

....

....

Putting it into practice

● What sort of put-downs get to you?

....

....

● Who are the people who use them?

....

....

● What will you say when they next use this approach?

....

....

- Next time you are annoyed by a put-down, respond calmly and assertively.

Handling put-downs: Model answers

The following are *examples* of answers. It is highly unlikely that you will have these 'word for word' but your answer should be similar in length, not have extra justifying phrases and be similar in tone.

1. 'I'll think about that, but I need to make up my own mind.'
2. 'No, are you in a hurry?'
3. 'What do you need me for?'
4. 'I don't see it as stupid.'
5. 'I wouldn't know about other women, but it is my opinion.'
6. 'I believe he did.'
7. 'How should we approach it?'

Moving on

11

Receiving criticism

It is seldom that people enjoy giving criticism and their awkward-ness in doing so may make them behave in a non-assertive or aggressive manner. Non-assertive criticism is difficult to handle because it is often not clear what is wrong and what improvements are required. Aggressive criticism leaves you feeling put down, even humiliated and can severely dent your self-confidence.

Even when criticism is given well, to be on the receiving end is not usually an enjoyable experience and it takes your assertive skills to face it realistically and come out of it with your self-esteem intact and, if necessary, a clear plan for change and improvement.

Rights and Responsibilities

You have the Right to:
- privacy;
- make mistakes;
- not understand.

You have the Responsibility to:
- listen;
- consider valid criticism.

The other person may have the responsibility to criticize you. For example, a manager is responsible for the work of a department and will have to ensure that all staff work efficiently and accurately. This may involve criticism (hopefully constructive) when things go wrong.

However, no one has the right to make the criticism a personal attack or put you down as a person for one mistake or problem. It is important to remember that to have one aspect of your work criticized does not make you a failure as a whole.

Listen to what the other person is saying and try to separate the facts (valid criticism) from personal attack. If you feel it is the latter, point it out and ask for the criticism to be directed at the facts.

'This Reception is chaotic; there are papers everywhere, that

coffee-cup is empty and shouldn't be seen anyway. You sit there reading the newspaper or chatting; the whole thing is a mess and you have no sense of responsibility to the company.'

'I feel a great sense of responsibility to the company but accept that this is untidy. Can we keep to that fact and sort out how it could be improved? For example, some trays would mean I could keep the papers in order.'

If you are unclear about the criticism, you should ask for examples but make sure you do so assertively and not as though issuing a challenge.

'I was not aware of chatting or reading the paper. Can you give me some examples?'

If you disagree with the criticism, you should say so, but again not in a defensive, challenging manner. Clear 'I' statements (e.g. 'As I see it . . .' or 'I believe . . .') will help you keep an assertive approach.

Criticism that does not take the situation forward is a waste of time. There should be a clear agreement of changes that will be made and the best way of making them. If the other person is not making any move to do this but is dwelling on the criticism, you may like to ask questions to ensure that you understand the facts and then agree changes.

'As I understand it, you would like me to ensure that the Reception area is tidied and I should arrange cover so that I take my lunch break in the canteen and can read my paper there.'
'Well, yes, that seems to be it.'
'That's fine. And you'll order me two sets of trays so that the typing and mail can be sorted tidily?'
'Yes, I'll do that.'

Valid criticism

Valid criticism is that which you accept to be right. You did forget to mend your child's sports bag, you were late for lunch at your parents', the letter you typed did have several mistakes in it, etc.

Do not forget that you have the Right to make mistakes or not to understand but that this is countered by the Responsibility to learn from your mistakes and to try not to repeat them.

It is easy to get defensive or to want to hide from our mistakes but in terms of assertive skills it is important to accept them and take responsibility. Many of us will use any terms rather than admit to our fault, yet it is a powerful aide to apology.

'I'm sorry, I completely forgot it.'

'I'm sorry to be late, I just did not get organized.'

'I'm sorry about the mistakes, I wasn't concentrating.'

Of course, all these assume a genuine apology and a clear intent to put the mistakes right and not repeat them.

Beware of letting your non-verbal behaviour show your discomfort when being criticized. Maintain eye contact and keep your voice steady, neither sinking nor becoming shrill.

Exercise

Identify two occasions when you have been criticized and your feelings at the time. How did you react? What should you have said and/or done?

Occasion: ....

Feelings: ....

Reaction: ....

With hindsight, I should have: ....

....

Occasion: ....

Feelings: ....

Reaction: ....

With hindsight, I should have: ....

....

Putting it into practice

- Look at your response to Questions 10 and 11 of Section 2, 'In preparation . . .' and consider your answers in the light of this Section.

- How do you *feel* when criticized? ....
....
....

- What effect do these feelings have on your body language and behaviour?

....
....

- Identify the points that are particularly relevant to you for when you are next criticized.

....
....
....

12

Giving criticism

Giving criticism covers many things from telling off the children to carrying out a performance appraisal at work.

Criticism is often seen as a negative thing – stopping someone from doing something wrong, rather than helping them to get it right. In fact, if no correction and guidance were given, it would be difficult to make improvements.

Rights and Responsibilities

You have the Right to:
- criticize (or do you?);
- have your criticism taken seriously.

You have the Responsibility to:
- be fair and honest;
- ensure it is not a personal attack.

A practical approach

GIVE THE CRITICISM IN PRIVATE

Even the most valid comments will not be received well in front of an audience. It is also important not to make an issue of 'come-into-my-office-for-a-moment' style. It is embarrassing for anyone to be picked out in this way and feel the eyes of colleagues or family upon them.

KEEP THE CRITICISM BALANCED

No one is all bad, even if it seems that way in the heat of the moment. To concentrate only on the aspects you want changed will demoralize the person. Acknowledge someone's good points or the effort they have made to help them retain their self-esteem and keep the criticism in perspective.

AVOID PERSONAL ATTACKS

Before you criticize anyone, make sure you are clear in your own mind about the problem. Even though you may feel sure of someone's motives, it is important to keep to facts. Consider examples that support your criticism. You may not need, or wish, to use these but they help keep the problem in perspective. Make sure that you stick to the facts and do not allow yourself to make broad generalizations or to drag in other complaints which will often not be relevant.

'Several of your letters contain typing mistakes; I have had to return two out of three for correction over the past week.'
not
'All your letters are full of mistakes – what's wrong with you?'

DO NOT EXAGGERATE

Avoid using general or exaggerated statements. They not only make the criticism less clear but are likely to annoy or upset the person being criticized, and if they become defensive, they are less likely to take the criticism on board.

'You have been late at least twice each week over the last month.'
not
'You are always late.'

'I find your behaviour annoying.'
not
'You infuriate everyone.'

Constructive criticism

Begin by considering what you want to achieve by making the criticism and be sure that you are asking for something that the other person can comply with or give.

Choose examples that are relevant and think about how you can phrase them so that they do not become a personal attack.

Identify the good points or achievements of the person being criticized in order to keep a reasonable balance.

When you come to speak to the person, make sure that you introduce the subject clearly and come to the point quickly. Find out the other person's views of the situation; you may find it helps to let them know that you can see their point of view but that their actions, work, etc. are not acceptable.

It is preferable to ask the other person for possible solutions – they will be far more committed to their own ideas than to something you lay down, and they can't later claim that you set them an unachievable target.

Be sure that you both agree, in clear terms, the changes that are to be made and if necessary, the ways and time-scale in which they will be made. It will also help to agree to review progress in a given period of time.

This may sound fine for a planned appraisal but far too involved for getting a teenager to tidy his room. However, the general principles still apply and to take a few moments to consider even the most minor criticism will reduce the chances of it becoming nagging.

Exercise

Identify three situations when you might have to criticize someone. These can be everyday situations, such as tackling a child about an untidy bedroom or the volume of their radio, criticism at work, or any other situation with friends, family or colleagues.

For each, identify when it would be best to tackle them, how you will introduce the subject and some ideas for words you can use to make the criticism.

Situation: ....

....

When to talk to them: ....

Introduction: ....

....

Ideas for suitable wording: ....

....

....

Situation: ....

....

When to talk to them: ....

Introduction: ....

....

Ideas for suitable wording: ....

....

....

Situation: ....

....

When to talk to them: ....

Introduction: ....

....

Ideas for suitable wording: ....

....

....

Putting it into practice

- Look at your response to Questions 12 and 13 of Section 2, 'In preparation . . .' and consider your answers in the light of this Section.

- When do you criticize others? ....

....

....

- How do you feel when you criticize someone (may be a variety of different feelings depending on the situations).

....

....

- What effect do these feelings have on your body language and behaviour?

....

....

- Identify the points that are particularly relevant to you for when you are next criticized.

....

....

....

13

People problems

The problem with facing up to 'people problems' is that, by virtue of the fact that it is a problem and thus creating difficulties for us, we are likely to be either non-assertive or aggressive when tackling the person who is the cause.

If we are to get others to change their behaviour, it is necessary to approach them in a calm and controlled manner. We have to be clear about what the problem is and be able to put it over to the other person in such a way that we minimize the risk of their becoming defensive. This self-control implies the avoidance of tears and tantrums and the ability to stick to the point rather than bringing in all past problems, clouding the issue and ending up with a full-scale row.

The assertive approach to 'people problems' implies thinking clearly about the problem and its effects, looking at the Rights and Responsibilities of both parties. Basically, you are making a request of someone – that they change their behaviour with regard to a particular issue. In many ways, the principle is the same as in the earlier chapter on making requests, but because the issues tend to be more complicated, so the approach is a little more detailed.

It is essential to plan what you want to say, and, just as importantly, what not to say. You will need to practise saying it so that it comes naturally and you are not easily put off. Finally, you will need to plan where you say it: do you want to make formal arrangements to see someone, arrange to 'bump into them', or prepare what you will say next time they exhibit the behaviour you want them to change.

Stage 1: Preparation

Note down a clear description of the problem and identify precisely *why* it is a problem to you. Decide what you want done about it and assess what the views of the other party are likely to be.

The problem is that my two children disappear after tea without giving any help with the clearing up. Although their excuses are valid (homework, etc.) I think they could help if they were willing. It's a problem because:

– I'm tired after work;
– I resent having to clear up alone;
– I'm annoyed with myself for nagging them unproductively.

I want us to clear up together which will save a considerable amount of time and I think will benefit us through working together as a team.

(This example is carried through below.)

Stage 2: Decide when to tackle the person

Timing is vital. There is no point in initiating a major discussion when the other party is tired or under pressure. If at work, you need to decide whether formally to book an appointment to see the problem person, whether to engineer a meeting 'over the photo-copier' or whether to plan your approach as a response when the problem next occurs.

'I will raise the issue when we're talking during tea.'

Stage 3: Plan what to say

Although you know what you're talking about, it is likely to come out of the blue to the other party. Therefore, you should plan how to introduce the subject. After this, you should explain why it is a problem to you before asking for the changes you want the other person to make. Finally, it will help you achieve the change if you can show the other person what they will gain from meeting you half-way.

The structure below seems long and involved but once you have worked through it and used it to organize your thoughts, you will find that it is not difficult to shorten it. At first it will sound stilted and will obviously be 'written' not 'spoken' English. The idea is that by the time you tackle the person, it has become a fluent short paragraph using words and phrases that are natural to you. Reading it aloud throughout all the stages of preparation will help you achieve this.

The final 'speech' should comprise a maximum of four sentences (often it will be less) and not be longer than a paragraph. If you allow it to be long and wordy, you will lose your essential message and increase your chances of getting side-tracked.

INTRODUCE

- Be specific and simple. *'When you stare out of the window while I'm talking . . .'*
- Describe the person's actions, not motives or intentions. As above, rather than *'When you try to put me off by staring out of the window while I'm talking . . .'*
- Try to avoid accusative 'you' statements. *'When you go off to watch the news . . .'*

   'When we have finished tea, I always clear up alone.'

IMPACT

(the effect it has on you)
- Acknowledge and take responsibility for your feelings. *'I feel . . .'* not *'You make me feel . . .'*
- Be calm and specific. *'I feel angry/humiliated/embarrassed'* not *'I feel funny.'*

   'I resent this because I am tired at that time and have lots to do before your father gets home.'

INFORM

(the person of the changes you would like made)
- Be clear and direct.
- Be realistic.
- Leave room for negotiation. *'How do you feel about this. . . ?'*
- Recognize that the other person has feelings. *'I understand that you . . .'*

   'I would prefer that we clear up together which will only take 15 minutes.'

INCENTIVE

(what is in it for the other person if they agree)
- Ensure that it will be seen as a benefit to the other person.
- Offer something that you will deliver.

Although I am asking them because I need the help and I would like to get them to take responsibility in the house, this is not a great incentive to them, therefore I will use: *'This will mean I have time to help with your homework/drive you to football practice, whatever.'*

You may like to consider the actions you will take if the other party refuses to change. Be careful as this is a threat and there is always the risk that you will have to do as you have threatened. If you follow this route, you should be clear, direct and keep your threat appropriate to the behaviour.

'I will leave the clearing up to you on alternate nights' or 'I will not be available at all for homework/football practice.'

The examples above run into a short, clear statement leaving the threat to use only if necessary.

'When we have finished tea, I always clear up alone. I resent this because I am tired at that time and have lots to do before your father gets home. I would prefer that we clear up together which will only take 15 minutes, which will mean that I have the time to drive you to the football club.'

The following are three more examples of this approach.

Example 1

Problem: A friend who calls uninvited. It is a problem because I

feel I have to offer her coffee, even though it might be inconvenient to me.

When you call in to see me unexpectedly (INTRO-DUCE), I feel annoyed because my work is interrupted (IMPACT); please could you ring first so that I can plan a break or arrange a different time (INFORM). This will mean we can have a decent chat and you will have my undivided attention (INCENTIVE).

Example 2

Problem: A colleague who tends to speak in my place at meetings.

When we attend meetings together, you often take over when I am speaking (INTRODUCE). This irritates me (IMPACT) and I would prefer that you let me finish speaking before adding any comments you wish to make (INFORM). This will improve the image we portray as a team and mean that you can concentrate on your topics (INCENTIVE).

Example 3

Problem: A friend who dominates the choice about what we do on our evening out.

When we go out, I seldom get to express an opinion as to where we should go (INTRODUCE). I feel frustrated as there are a couple of films I would like to see (IMPACT). Please can we take it in turns to choose what we do (INFORM). I will then continue to go out with you regularly (INCENTIVE).

Exercise

If you would like more practice in preparing scripts, the following are three examples you can work through.

Problem: At the beginning of term, you and your neighbour agreed a school run. Since then she has regularly called you at short notice and asked you to take her turn. When you needed to ask her to cover your run, she said she was not able to that day. You feel you are doing far more than your share and the short notice changes are often inconvenient. You would like to cancel the share or return to the original plan.

Introduce ....
....
....

Impact ....
....
....

Inform ....
....
....

Incentive ....
....
....

Problem: Your manager keeps disappearing from her office without telling you that she is going or how long she will be. You find it embarrassing when you tell callers she is in, only to find she is not and it makes you look inefficient when you do not know when she will be in. You would like her to keep you informed.

Introduce ....
....
....

Impact ....
....
....

Inform ....
....
....

Incentive ....

....

....

Problem: A teenage child who has started to spend all evening on the telephone. You are concerned because of the expense and because it prevents incoming calls and your use of the phone. You are happy to pay for short calls, but would like a fairer use of the telephone.

Introduce ....

....

....

Impact ....

....

....

Inform ....

....

....

Incentive ....

....

....

Putting it into practice

- Refer back to Questions 14 and 15 of Section 2, 'In Preparation . . .'. Which of these people would you most like to approach regarding their behaviour?

....

- Before tackling the next Section consider the problem and what changes you would like made for each.

1. General thoughts ....

   ....

   ....

   Specific and realistic changes ....

   ....

   ....

2. General thoughts ....

   ....

   ....

   Specific and realistic changes ....

   ....

   ....

3. General thoughts ....

   ....

   ....

   Specific and realistic changes ....

   ....

   ....

People problems: Model answers

The following are *examples*, it is highly unlikely that you will match these 'word for word' but your answer should be similar in length, not have extra justifying phrases and be similar in tone.

1. When you ask me to take over your school run at short notice (INTRODUCE) I feel resentful because I often have to alter my plans (IMPACT). I would prefer that we stick to the days we agreed (INFORM) then I will be happy to continue to share the run (INCENTIVE).

2. When I am unable to find you (INTRODUCE) I am embarrassed because we look so disorganized in front of clients

(IMPACT). Please could you tell me when you leave your office and when you expect to return (INFORM) which will make us appear much more efficient and mean we provide a better customer service (INCENTIVE).

3. When you make long telephone calls to friends (INTRO-DUCE) I feel annoyed because of the cost and because no one else can use the phone (IMPACT). I would prefer that you limit the call time to five minutes (INFORM). I will then be happy to continue to pay for your calls (INCENTIVE).

14

Tackling a problem

Having decided on the problem you would like to tackle, you need to plan your approach. To help you do this, complete the questions below.

Name of problem person: ....

Description of problem: ....

Why is it a problem to me? (Be honest!): ....

....

What words describe my feelings? ....

What do I want the problem person to do? ....

Why should they be bothered to change? (What's in it for them?): ..

....

Do I want to tackle them: ☐ formally ☐ informally ☐ next time they 'sin'?

Using your answers above, write one sentence in each of the sections below. You may find it useful to refer to the notes in the last Section.

Introduction
The explanation of the problem/situation:

....

....

....

Impact
The effect it has on you:

....

....

....

Inform
The changes you would like made:

....

....

....

Incentive
What the other person will gain by changing:

....

....

....

Threat
In case all else fails (remember it is preferable not to use this, but worth considering – it helps put the problem into perspective):

....

....

....

Putting it into practice

- Read through your first four sentences a few times, adjusting the wording so that it sounds natural when you say it aloud, then rewrite it as a paragraph below. It is essential to use words that you would use naturally; it should be spoken English rather than written. Space is given to allow a few rewrites!

....

....

....

....

....

....

....

....

....

....

....

....

....

....

....

....

....

....

- Keep a note of the paragraph with you so that you can keep returning to it with improvements.

15

Reactions to your assertiveness

The examples below all relate to your plan. However you will find them equally applicable in day-to-day dealings with people when faced with non-assertive or aggressive behaviour.

- Firstly rewrite your paragraph below.

  Introduction: ....

  ....

  Impact: ....

  ....

  Inform: ....

  ....

  Incentive: ....

  ....

- Visualize yourself presenting this to the problem person.

  Where will you be? ....

  How will you be standing/sitting? ....

  What will you be wearing? ....

- Now consider how they will react to each stage (for example, polite amusement? genuine interest? interruptions? annoyance?). Describe the reactions you expect and identify any flashpoints where they may interrupt.

  ....

  ....

....

....

● Sometimes the problem person will agree to your request with no complaint. They may ask a couple of questions through a genuine lack of understanding or in anticipation of a problem. However, on other occasions you may have to face aggressive or defensive barriers and it is important to be able to maintain an assertive approach in the face of these behaviours.

Common deflections

The following are some of the more common deflective responses.

THE PUT-OFF

The receiver tries to defer the discussion, usually before you have got into your stride. Use your judgement to decide whether they are under genuine time pressure with some other matter or simply do not want to listen to you.

'Some other time, I'm busy.'

'I don't have the time to waste arguing with you, the matter is closed.'

THE DENIAL

A flat denial of what you're saying can draw you into an argument. It is important not to let yourself be side-tracked.

'That's not true.'

BLAMING

This might involve shifting the blame back on to you or diverting attention to a third party.

'That's because you do not listen to me.'

'It's because he had a go at me.'

'You are just too sensitive.'

JOKING

This often takes the form of sarcasm or a 'light' response which belittles your statement.

'I've only nagged you three times? I must be off form.'

YOU'VE HURT ME

This might be a direct accusation, implication or tears. Although it may be non-assertion, beware of manipulative aggression – trying to make you feel guilty.

'By saying that, you've really upset me.'

EXCESSIVE APOLOGIZING

This can lead you into thinking that you have gained the agreement of the other party when in fact, unless you agree future behaviour, you have gained nothing.

'Oh, how awful; I'm sorry; I really am (etc.).'

APPARENT AGREEMENT

This deflection involves the receiver apparently agreeing with you. They listen and seem ready to agree with your proposals but do not actually make the decision. Unlike the put-off, this approach deceives you into believing you've made progress.

'Very interesting. Let me think about it.'

'Let me check it out and I'll get back to you.'

Putting it into practice

The next Section deals with handling these deflections. Before that, return to your planned approach and visualize delivering your statement. What type of non-assertive or aggressive responses are you likely to receive and at which points? Make a note of these below.

16

Overcoming the barriers

The key to overcoming the barriers that others may put in the path of your assertiveness is to LISTEN. You need to:

- Adopt an interested and attentive body language (calm, relaxed, steady eye contact).
- Ignore any personal comments and any other irrelevant statements.
- Ignore the tone of voice (angry, patronizing, etc.).
- Concentrate and respond to the words that are spoken (not the tone that is used).

For example if you are faced with 'What am I supposed to do about your problem?' said in a patronizing way, you should calmly answer the question, 'What should I do?' (probably by restating the INFORM section).

Regrettably, there is no textbook response for each of the barriers discussed in the last Section as every receiver responds differently. The following suggestions work well in a variety of situations and if you familiarize yourself with them you will find they come readily when needed.

PERSIST

Repeat the main point, usually the 'Inform' line. This is also known as the 'broken record' technique.

'That's not true.'
'It's how I see it; I would prefer that we . . .'

STRESS YOUR FEELINGS

Restate your 'Impact' line to emphasize the effect on you. It often helps to take the discussion forward in the same sentence.

'You're making a mountain out of a molehill.'
'I'm upset about it and would like to talk it through with you.'

YES, BUT . . .

Agree that the other person has the Right to their view, but disagree that you should hold the same view.

'I appreciate that you want Toby to follow you into the business, but he's very keen to travel and I think he should take the chance while he can.'

ASK A QUESTION

Do not accept a vague response. Ask an open question for clarification.

'Very interesting. Let me think about it.'
'How long do you need? I'll call in to see you.'

DISAGREE

A straightforward statement – 'I do not see it that way.'

'Hannah is the best person for the job, we should promote her.'
'I don't think so; we need someone with supervisory experience.'

DISMISS

Deny the relevance of the deflection and take the discussion on to avoid being sidetracked into an argument.

'You are just too sensitive.'
'I don't think that's relevant; I'd like to be allowed to voice my own opinion.'

It is important to maintain your assertive body language and avoid any anger creeping into your voice. If you can remain warm and friendly (even when you do not feel it) you can keep the discussion on the topic and avoid irrelevant argument.

Exercise

The following are a selection of assertive statements, followed by an aggressive or non-assertive reaction. For each, respond assertively to that reaction.

'I'd like to discuss the problem we had last week.'

'Some other time, I'm busy.'

....

....

....

'When you are late, I feel annoyed because I have to cover for you.'

'I couldn't care less.'

....

....

....

'Have you read through my short story competition entry?'

'No, I wasn't ready for a joke.'

....

....

....

In response to your statement, the receiver bursts into tears.

....

....

....

In response to your statement, the receiver reels off a string of apologies which start to make you feel guilty.

....

....

....

You have delivered your statement and the receiver responds with 'That sounds a useful idea, let me think it over'.

....
....
....

Putting it into practice

- Return to your statement and anticipated deflections. How will
  you respond to each? Remember to consider both body language
  and the words you can use.

Deflection: ....

....

Reaction: ....

....

....

Deflection: ....

....

Reaction: ....

....

....

Deflection: ....

....

Reaction: ....

....

....

Deflection: ....

....

Reaction: ....

....

....

- Although you cannot guarantee how the other person will react, familiarize yourself with these techniques and you will be able to overcome most negative responses.

- When you are happy with your statement and confident that you can keep your cool and respond positively to the deflections, find a suitable moment and take the plunge. Remember, if you don't try, you won't succeed.

Overcoming the objections: Model answers

1. When would be convenient to you?
2. Maybe not, but we must sort it out.
3. It's important to me; I would be grateful if you could give it a serious look-over.
4. Why don't we continue this conversation after lunch when you've had time to get yourself together? Or
   I'm sorry this is upsetting you, but we must clear it up.
5. Thank you for your apology. Are you happy with the suggestion I've made?
6. I'll call in and see you on Monday morning to find out what you think.

17

Troubleshooting

This Section is different from the others in that it is not intended to be used until or unless you find that your assertiveness does not work; when you have tried to be assertive but have not managed it! It doesn't matter whether the issue is large or small, if you allow yourself to dwell on your 'failure' you're wasting time and energy and are just building up a negative image of yourself.

It is highly unlikely that you will manage to behave assertively in every situation, particularly when you start to develop your skills. The way you react when you have not managed to behave assertively has a great effect on the way in which your skills continue to develop.

If you allow your experience to 'prove you can't do it', it will be a self-fulfilling prophecy and it will be even more difficult to assert yourself next time. On the other hand, if you look objectively and constructively at the situation, at your feelings at the time, and realistically at your behaviour, you will be able to use it as a learning process. If you can identify why you went wrong, you can identify how you want to behave next time and plan how you can do so.

No matter how unimportant the situation, if you feel you have not succeeded in behaving assertively when you wanted, take time to work through the following questions. It will help just as much with major problems as with minor. Make sure that you are honest with yourself and, if you feel it is necessary, ask a partner, friend or colleague for their views. Try to use specific words and phrases that accurately describe the situation as you saw it.

There is space here for dealing with one occasion; just use a blank sheet when you need to work through it again in the future.

1. Outline the circumstances and situation (you may not believe it but you might not remember what it was all about a year from now!).

   ....

   ....

   ....

2. Describe your behaviour specifically and honestly (the aspects you were pleased with as well as the ones you were not).

....

....

....

....

3. Describe the behaviour of the other person (again, specifically and honestly).

....

....

....

....

4. Were there any other relevant circumstances? (e.g. Had you had a disagreement with someone else? Was there anything else worrying you? Were you already late or under some similar pressure?)

....

....

....

....

5. Describe you body language. (e.g. How were you sitting/ standing? Were you mumbling or shouting? Were you looking at the other person, or staring at them, or could you not meet their eyes?)

....

....

....

....

6. Give examples of things that were said in the conversation, by

both parties. How would you describe these? (e.g. rude, defensive, unclear meaning.)

....

....

....

7. Ideally, what did you want to be the outcome of the exchange?

....

....

....

And what would be an acceptable compromise, or what would you be prepared to give?

....

....

....

8. Define the changes you would like to make to your body language. Be specific.

> *'I must look directly at her eyes most of the time.'*
>   not
> *'Better eye contact.'*

....

....

....

....

9. Define the changes you would like to make to the words you said and the way in which you said them. Again, be specific.

....

....

....

10. Identify the three key points to bear in mind to help to remain assertive when you next face a similar situation.

....

....

....

....

....

....

It might be too late to have another go at the same situation. It is still worth working through this exercise because your ideas for improvements will help you when you next face a difficult conversation. Obviously, if you can have another try, then you should do so and see what changes a more assertive approach will bring.

Whatever happens, make sure that you continue with your day-to-day assertiveness. This will help you build your confidence for future difficult situations and combined with a review of your thoughts above will enable you to tackle them when they arise.

18
Taking it forward

To reiterate a point made at the beginning of this workbook, 'assertive' does not describe a person, it describes their behaviour at a particular time.

As you have worked through this book, you will have seen ways in which you wish to change your behaviour. Through the 'Putting it into practice' sections, you will already have increased your assertiveness. Don't worry if you feel you have not made enough progress. Some people find they can build their skills very quickly, whilst others may take months to be assertive in the most basic situations. This is not failure! To be a little bit assertive when you find it very difficult is just as much of an achievement as tackling a major problem for someone who finds it easier.

Using the questions below, identify when you are already assertive and the situations and people with whom it will be easiest to increase your assertiveness. These should be the next steps in effecting continuing change.

These 'easy' situations are those in which you are most likely to succeed in early days and this success will build your self-esteem and confidence – vital if you are to develop your assertive skills. Note your successes, however minor, in the back of this book and use them to remind yourself that you can do it.

You will find that, with practice, you become generally assertive on a day-to-day basis and that your dealings with others become easier and more successful. The ease with which you make and receive compliments and requests and your ability to say no when you wish, and even handle criticism from others, will allow your confidence to grow and others will come to see you as an assertive and reasonable person. You can then turn to tackling others about their behaviour, using the 'People problems' approach outlined earlier.

Listen to yourself and note when you 'get it wrong' – behaving in a way that is different from that in which you want to. Remind yourself that this does not make you a failure as a person and turn to identifying what caused you to behave in this way.

e.g.   What was it that made you grovel?
What did they say that made you lose your temper?
With the benefit of hindsight, how should you have
behaved?

To do this in writing will help, and then bear this in mind next time
you face the situation.

In conclusion, remember that assertiveness is a skill; one that can
be learnt (even from scratch) and developed throughout life. You
will only gain from increased assertiveness. So take the risk and go
for it – try the assertive approach.

Questions

In column 1 list the ten people, by name, with whom you deal most
often (partner, children, family, friends, colleagues, doctor/
solicitor, and so on). Identify how they generally behave towards
you in Column 2. Identify how you generally behave with them in
Column 3.

	Column 1	Column 2	Column 3
1.	....	....	....
2.	....	....	....
3.	....	....	....
4.	....	....	....
5.	....	....	....
6.	....	....	....
7.	....	....	....
8.	....	....	....
9.	....	....	....
10.	....	....	....

For each of the above, identify at least one specific change you would like to make to the way you behave towards them.

1. ....

2. ....

3. ....

4. ....

5. ....

6. ....

7. ....

8. ....

9. ....

10. ....

Identify which three of the ten are your top priorities and how you are going to start changing your behaviour to achieve your target.

1. ....

....

2. ....

....

3. ....

....

For these three, what will be your ongoing changes in behaviour?

1. ....

....

2. ....

....

3. ....

....

What changes are you going to make to your body language to give
the impression of an assertive, confident person?

....

....

What general changes are you going to make to the type of things
you say?

....

....

Index